CW00740422

The
MagPi
ESSENTIALS

WELCOME TO

EXPERIMENT WITH THE SENSE HAT

Space exploration is fascinating and inspiring for children and adults alike. With the tiny Raspberry Pi computer helping to change the world little-by-little, it was only a matter of time before it went to space to help out there as well. This new adventure is called the Astro Pi project. To help the Raspberry Pi in its extraterrestrial mission, the Sense HAT was created to provide more functionality; the Sense HAT board sits on top of the Raspberry Pi, and has lights and sensors to allow the Pi to interact with the outside world.

In this book, we aim to help you figure out exactly what the Sense HAT is and how you could use it to make your projects and dreams a reality. It's an incredibly versatile and flexible bit of kit with plenty of very obvious uses, along with many many less-obvious ones, that you'll love to make and share.

Rob Zwetsloot
Features Editor, Raspberry Pi

FIND US ONLINE raspberrypi.org/magpi GET IN TOUCH magpi@raspberrypi.org

EDITORIAL
Managing Editor: Russell Barnes
russell@raspberrypi.org
Features Editor: Rob Zwetsloot
Sub Editors: Lorna Lynch, Laura Clay & Phil King

DESIGN
Critical Media: criticalmedia.co.uk
Head of Design: Dougal Matthews
Designers: Lee Allen, Mike Kay

Available on the App Store

DISTRIBUTION
Seymour Distribution Ltd
2 East Poultry Ave,
London
EC1A 9PT | +44 (0)207 429 4000

THE MAGPI SUBSCRIPTIONS
Select Publisher Services Ltd
PO Box 6337, Bournemouth
BH1 9EH | +44 (0)1202 586 848
magpi.cc/Subs1

In print, this product is made using paper sourced from sustainable forests and the printer operates an environmental management system which has been assessed as conforming to ISO 14001.

This book is published by Raspberry Pi (Trading) Ltd., Mount Pleasant House, Cambridge, CB3 0RN. The publisher, editor and contributors accept no responsibility in respect of any omissions or errors relating to goods, products or services referred to or advertised in this product.

ISSN: 2051-9982.

The MagPi ESSENTIALS

CONTENTS

[THE PI EDUCATION TEAM]

Some of the articles you're about to read were created by the fantastic Raspberry Pi education team, a selection of excellent individuals who love to teach teachers how to use the Raspberry Pi. As well as seeing their work at Picademies around the world, they also write teaching materials which can be found online and in The MagPi magazine. You can read many more of their tutorials and lessons on the Resources section of the Raspberry Pi website: **raspberrypi.org/resources**

[CHAPTER ONE] WHAT IS THE SENSE HAT?

The special add-on to the Raspberry Pi that lets it interact more with the world around, as seen on the ISS!

The Raspberry Pi can do a lot of things thanks to its size, portability, and ability to connect to the internet easily. With the GPIO ports you can control electronics and interact with the world. One of the best ways of doing this is by using an add-on like the Sense HAT.

The Sense HAT is a very sophisticated add-on board for the Raspberry Pi. While HAT is an acronym (Hardware Attached on-Top), it does act in a way like a hat for your Raspberry Pi. The Sense HAT contains a suite of sensors that allows the Raspberry Pi to sense the world around it, along with an array of LEDs on top which can be used to display information on what the board can sense, and a little joystick.

The Sense HAT is a vital component of the Astro Pi, the specially adapted educational Raspberry Pis which were sent up to the International Space Station with British ESA astronaut Tim Peake to run code created by children.This wasn't what the HAT was originally designed for, though, as the Sense HAT's Project Lead Jonathan Bell explains:

"I sort of hijacked a pet project of James [Adams's] and turned it into a space-faring board," says Jonathan. James Adams is the Director of Hardware at Raspberry Pi, and along with Jonathan, was one of the main driving forces behind the Sense HAT.

Above British ESA astronaut Tim Peake, who will be using the Sense HAT on the ISS for various experiments created by school children

"Effectively we wanted to produce a board that would be a neat, fun example of how to design a HAT" Jonathan continued. "It was an exercise in how to design a HAT which could be put into mass-production: how would somebody go about doing that so hundreds of thousands of HATs could be made, and how would we design the board to deal with that."

Half-way through development, what was once a relatively basic HAT had some sensors added to it, similar to the kind used on mobile phones. "Eventually we said, hang on a minute, what happens if we put loads of sensors on this thing and turn it into a kind of a cool toy!"

When the Sense HAT was eventually completed, it had three key sensors: separate pressure and humidity sensors that can also both measure temperature, and a motion sensor that contained an accelerometer, a gyroscope, and a magnetometer. As mentioned before, these sensors are joined by the 8 x 8 LED screen and the joystick.

Each sensor, the LED screen, and the joystick can all work independently of each other as well as all together at once. You could simply have the LED screen display little images for you, or have the Sense HAT keep track of the temperature throughout the day; it's very flexible to use!

All of this is accessible on the Raspberry Pi by just popping the Sense HAT on top of the the GPIO pins and using the right Python code, which is what the space-bound Astro Pis on the ISS are doing.

"The Astro Pi experiments make good use of the HAT itself," Jonathan told us. "Some of them in quite unusual ways. We have a few Easter eggs up there, which you'll have to find out about, but there have been some ingenious uses of the sensors. One of the experiments that caught our eye in terms of sensing was one that attempted to detect an astronaut. The astronaut detector sits there, monitoring the humidity, and if there is a certain percentage change in humidity in the module it thinks there's an astronaut present. It flashes a message on the LED matrix saying "Are you there?".

The Astro Pis also have a special metal case which allows them (after a few other tweaks to the Raspberry Pi) to be spaceworthy, and we'll talk much more about that in the section about the Astro Pi. A whole host of experiments designed by British school children went up with the Pi for Tim Peake to use, and the data from those experiments which make use of the Sense HAT will be sent down to Earth.

The Sense HAT is capable of many things thanks to inventive use of the sensors or even just the code that controls it, and in this special digital edition we hope to inspire you to create some cool projects of your own.

The Sense HAT costs £23/$39.95 and can be bought from the Swag Shop (**magpi.cc/SenseHAT**), Adafruit (**magpi.cc/1TGGFy6**) or from any other distributor listed on the Raspberry Pi website (**magpi.cc/1TGGUt5**).

Below The Sense HAT is quite small, but packs a large number of sensors and features

[CHAPTER TWO]

HIGH FLIERS

British ESA astronaut Tim Peake isn't the only Brit aboard the International Space Station. David Crookes looks at how the Pi got into the sky and what it means for future generations.

On 15 December, British ESA astronaut Tim Peake made history as the first British astronaut to visit the International Space Station. For the next six months, he will achieve most children's dreams as he lives and works 400 kilometres above the Earth to carry out a comprehensive science programme during a mission called Principia.

His role will be to run experiments using the unique environment of space and to try new technologies that may become crucial when humans begin to visit other planets such as Mars. But he will not be alone. Aside from living with five international colleagues, all of whom have spent years training for their difficult roles, Tim was greeted by another Brit, one set to accompany him throughout the whole of his time away from Earth.

That extra 'colleague' is, of course, the British-made Raspberry Pi which, by the time Tim set off on a Soyuz spacecraft from Russia's Baikonur cosmodrome in Kazakhstan, was already be waiting on board the ISS. Two Raspberry Pis were flown skywards on a Cygnus cargo freighter on 6 December, going ahead of Tim thanks to a lack of room on the Soyuz flight. But that meant the computers were ready and waiting to be unboxed by the time Tim arrived.

The Raspberry Pi's space adventure is referred to as the Astro Pi mission and, while it hasn't been an easy ride for those involved, it certainly has been rewarding. That's because the computers have each

ASTRO PI UP CLOSE

01 The most noticeable part of the Astro Pi assembly is the 8×8 RGB LED matrix on the Sense HAT. It has a 60fps refresh rate and 15-bit colour resolution.

02 The all-in-one gyroscope, accelerometer, and magnetometer will measure the orientation of objects, an increase in speed, and the strength and direction of a magnetic field.

03 A temperature and humidity sensor not only measures hot and cold, but the amount of water vapour in the air. It can detect whether a person is standing close by, for instance.

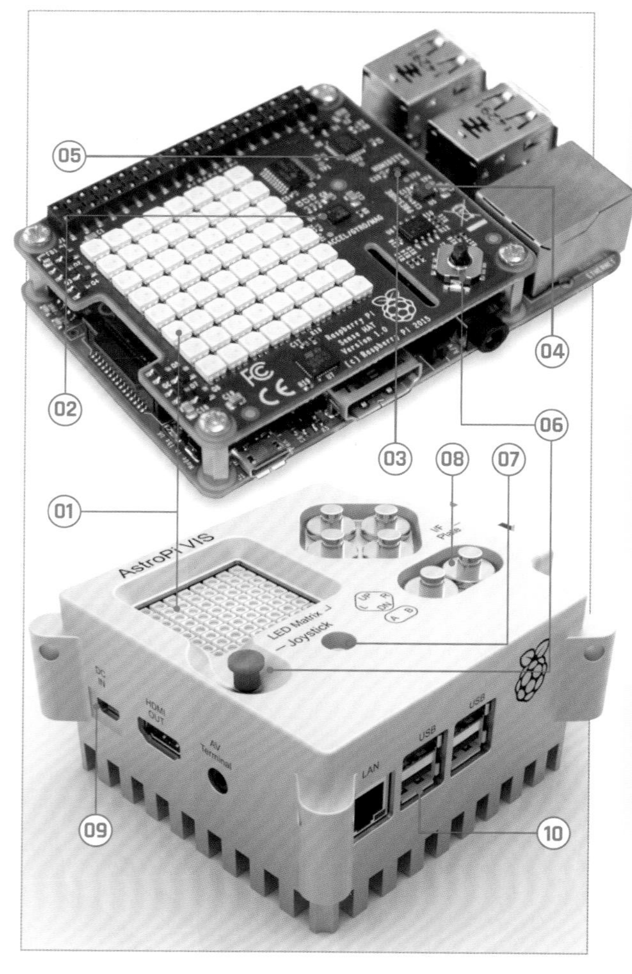

04 The barometric pressure sensor is able to measure the force exerted by small molecules in the air.

05 The graphics are driven by this microcontroller.

06 To allow the astronauts to navigate the screen and options, there is a five-button joystick which allows for up, down, left, and right movements, as well as an Enter via a click.

07 This hole allows air to enter the Astro Pi device, where it can be detected by the sensors and tested.

08 The actual casing is made from aerospace-grade aluminium and is said to have cost £3,000 to make.

09 As well as the various special components of the Sense HAT, the usual functions of the Raspberry Pi are used. This is the power socket.

10 Here we see the various connections of the Raspberry Pi, from USB sockets to LAN.

been equipped with Sense HAT expansion sensor board, and have been placed inside a cutting-edge aerospace case that has been built to withstand any conditions space will throw at it. As well as allowing the Raspberry Pi to measure the ISS's environment, follow its journey through space, and pick up the Earth's magnetic field, the mission will give schoolchildren the chance to have their code run in space for the first time ever. And that, says Tim, is proving to be most exciting of all.

"[Astro Pi] has got a great sensor suite with temperature, pressure, humidity sensors, all sorts of things on it," he told BBC television's *The One Show* following the final press conference on 6 November. "So, the schoolkids basically coded programs that I'm going to run on board the Space Station, and this Astro Pi is going to be in various different modules running an experiment each week. I'm going to send down the data so that during the mission they can see [it], see what they've managed to achieve, and if they need to modify the code, they can send it back up to me."

The Astro Pi was the brainchild of the UK Space Agency and the Raspberry Pi Foundation, although according to David Honess, the Foundation's education resource engineer, it was "a case of being in the right place at the right time". Libby Jackson, the UK Space Agency's astronaut flight education programme manager, was looking at ways to encourage children to think about the applications for space

Tim Peake (far right) attends the final press conference before launch

and the ISS. "When I was applying for my current role, the candidates were asked to prepare an idea for an activity that could inspire kids and at the time I knew about the Raspberry Pi," she says. "I didn't take that idea to the interview because I didn't know enough and I was afraid I'd be asked questions I couldn't answer."

The idea remained with her and when she was talking with UK Space, the UK space industry's trade association, she confessed she couldn't shake away the idea of having fun with the Raspberry Pi. "As it happened, someone mentioned that they had been talking to Eben Upton, the CEO of the Raspberry Pi Trading company, and so had a point of contact. A meeting was quickly set up," she says.

"The UK space industry wants to ensure that there are enough people in the future to hire to carry on..."

The momentum began building solidly. At this time, David had just begun working with the Raspberry Pi Foundation and Eben had sent a casual email asking if anyone fancied accompanying him to a meeting with Airbus Defence and Space. David volunteered and found that Dr Stuart Eves, Airbus's lead mission concepts engineer, was a passionate advocate of the Raspberry Pi. This resulted in the Pi Foundation being hooked up with Libby at the UK Space Agency: "We ended up in a meeting with the UK Space Agency and Tim Peake's mission was on the table..."

A decision was soon taken to exploit the possibilities of that mission as much as possible, and so the idea of a competition to engage schools was seized upon. The belief was that it could encourage schoolchildren to become more interested in space and open their eyes to its employment possibilities. "The bottom line is that the UK space industry wants to ensure that there are enough people in the future to hire to carry on doing what they are doing," explains David. "And we feel this is part of the answer."

Once the go-ahead had been given, it was time to work out how the project would run. For Libby, the aim was to attach as much as possible to the Pi – "I knew the history of getting education payloads on the ISS," she explains, hinting at the difficulties – but the problem was the tight schedule they had to work with. The Astro Pi mission was being put together around a year before the expected flight, so there was never going to be enough time to invite children to come up with an experiment and make it fly. "We turned things on their head and said if we fly the hardware as it exists and ask the kids what we should do with it, that would help in terms of time," Libby continues. "It seemed the perfect solution."

Pi in the sky

It is not the first time a bare-bones computer has gone into space (and it's not incidentally the Pi's debut either, given Dave Akerman's efforts in strapping Pis to high-altitude balloons and taking snapshots from the edge of space). But while Arduinos were the first to boldly go where no other widely accessible device had gone before (onto satellites orbiting the Earth), Astro Pi was created to be different.

Tim during training in the Soyuz TMA simulator

LIFE ON THE ISS

The Astro Pi is going to live on board the International Space Station until 2022, when it is envisaged the battery operating its real-time clock will finally run out of power. During those seven years, the Pi will be made available for use by numerous crews, starting with Tim Peake, whose mission is set to cross between Expedition 46 and 47 (the current crew are part of Expedition 44). But just what is life like on board the ISS, and how much time will Tim get to spend with the computer?

WAKE-UP

Like everyone else on board, Tim will adhere to the GMT time zone. He will wake each morning in a small soundproofed cabin, have his breakfast, and get down to work. "They commute by floating in, and they start with a meeting with the ground controller to catch up on the day," says Libby Jackson, the UK Space Agency's astronaut flight education programme manager. "Then they will carry on and do their science experiments."

WORKING DAY

Tim's days will closely follow our own working lives. He is set to spend his time with five other astronauts in an environment that is equivalent in size to a five-bedroom house, and he will typically work a Monday to Friday week, starting at 8am and finishing at 6pm

KEEPING FIT

Each day is carefully scheduled so that the astronauts' time on board is fully utilised, and that includes hours set aside for maintenance. But they must also have time for exercise. Without regular fitness sessions, they can suffer bone and muscle loss. "They have two hours of exercise each day," reveals Libby.

CHIT CHAT

It is also important that the astronauts get some time to socialise. It can, after all, be lonely in space. "They try to get an hour lunch break together, just like we would on Earth," says Libby, explaining that meal times balance vitamins and minerals. "Some days they manage it, other days they work through or they stagger it, but [eating together] is the aim."

GOODNIGHT

At the end of the day, they seek to wrap things up. "They have a meeting with the crew and say goodnight," says Libby. "They can enjoy free time and during the evening and weekends, the mission controllers try not to disturb the crew unless they really have to."

TIME FOR PI

But what do they get up to? "Some will watch movies, others will look out of the window or call friends and family," says Libby. "On Saturday morning they will clean the space station, but Tim will hope to spend the afternoon doing education, working with the Astro Pi. Sunday will be his day off, though."

"Never before have we had a situation where the crew of the space station are using the same machine as your kids," says David. "But this is that time: we created the Sense HAT add-on board for the Pi and we challenged schools to come up with computer science-based experiments that Tim would run on the space station."

The response from schoolchildren amazed everyone, not only in the quantity of entries but in their quality. There were stories of children coding during their lunch breaks and working after school. The chance of having their code in space was proving to be a great motivator, and narrowing the experiments down to just seven winners proved tricky. "It came down to the completeness of the ideas and the quality of the coding," reveals Libby. "The things the kids came up with are far more creative than adults."

Indeed, the winners are certainly impressive. The Cranmere Code Club run by teacher (and ***The MagPi*** writer) Richard Hayler at the Cranmere Primary School tests the humidity surrounding Astro Pi. If fluctuation is detected, it is a possible indicator that an astronaut

The International Space Station

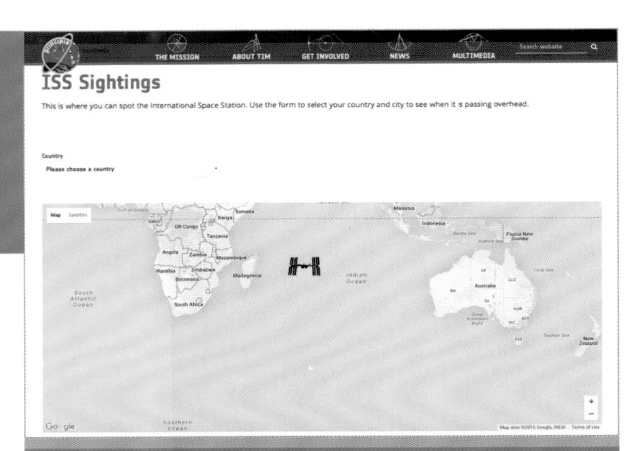

[SEE THE ISS WITH YOUR PI]

One of the great things about the ISS is that you are able to see it with your own eyes and without the aid of a telescope. The trick is knowing where it is in the sky at any given time, but there are apps and websites which allow you to follow it as it orbits 400 kilometres above Earth.

The Principia Mission website has an ISS spotter, which you can view by going to **principia.org.uk/iss-sightings**. There is also a Pi-based project called ISS Above, which can be hooked up to a TV to display the location of the ISS in real-time.

It began as a Kickstarter project and raised $17,731 from 199 backers, having originally asked for $5,000. Maker Liam Kennedy wanted to produce something which lit up whenever the ISS was nearby.

has come close, so the Pi will deliver a message on its 8×8 LED screen and take a photo via the camera, hoping to snap one of the ISS crew in action. "They are looking to see if humidity is a good indictor of the presence of the crew near the Astro Pi," David explains.

SpaceCRAFT is equally ingenious, with Hannah Belshaw from the Cumnor House Girls School suggesting using the output as a CSV file from the Astro Pi sensors within *Minecraft* so that the environmental measurements are represented in the game. "SpaceCRAFT logs all sensors to fill a massive CSV file and it works with code on the ground that plays it back in *Minecraft*," says David. Hannah dressed in a spacesuit to appear alongside Tim during his BBC interview.

One particular favourite among those involved with Astro Pi is Flags, created by Thirsk School under the watch of teacher Dan Aldred. The program uses telemetry data and the Astro Pi's real-time clock to work out the ISS's location. It searches its database to find the relevant flag and displays an image of it on the LED matrix with a phrase in the local language.

"It's lovely because the children have looked and thought about where the astronauts are in the world," says Libby. David agrees. "The crew will like it," he says. "The kids learned a lot about geography and they made the code recognise the boundaries of different countries. If it's above the sea, it shows a twinkly blue or green pattern."

Watchdog, by Kieran Wand at Cottenham Village College, makes good use of the Astro Pi sensors by measuring the temperature, pressure, and humidity on board the ISS, raising the alarm if they move outside acceptable parameters. Trees, by EnviroPi – a team at Westminster School – points the NoIR camera on the Astro Pi out of the window and allows it to take images of the ground, after which it can produce a Normalised Differentiated Vegetation Index (a measure of plant health).

Radiation, by the team Arthur, Alexander, and Kiran, overseen by Dr Jesse Peterson at Magdalen College School, uses the Camera Module of the Pi to detect radiation, measuring the intensity of tiny specks of light. But there is always time for fun, and so Lincoln UTC's Team Terminal, with teacher Mark Hall, have produced a suite of reaction games, together with a menu that the astronauts can use to select the one they fancy playing at that time.

Tim tries on a spacesuit

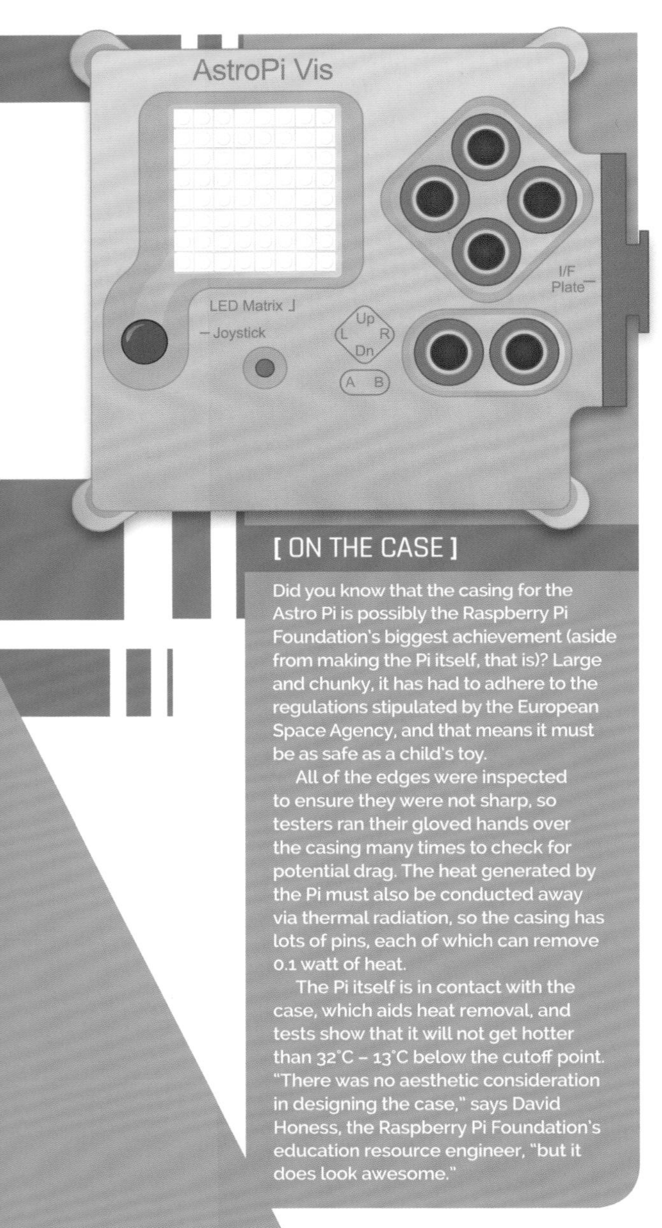

[ON THE CASE]

Did you know that the casing for the Astro Pi is possibly the Raspberry Pi Foundation's biggest achievement (aside from making the Pi itself, that is)? Large and chunky, it has had to adhere to the regulations stipulated by the European Space Agency, and that means it must be as safe as a child's toy.

All of the edges were inspected to ensure they were not sharp, so testers ran their gloved hands over the casing many times to check for potential drag. The heat generated by the Pi must also be conducted away via thermal radiation, so the casing has lots of pins, each of which can remove 0.1 watt of heat.

The Pi itself is in contact with the case, which aids heat removal, and tests show that it will not get hotter than 32°C – 13°C below the cutoff point. "There was no aesthetic consideration in designing the case," says David Honess, the Raspberry Pi Foundation's education resource engineer, "but it does look awesome."

Tim's role

Tim will be able to move between these experiments via an app on board the Astro Pi, called the Master Control Program (a nod to the 1982 movie *Tron*). But he doesn't have to keep checking it. The programs can run automatically. "There is a clock icon which will run program X for a set period," David explains. "It ensures the programs are run for the right amount of time."

Indeed, schedules have been specified, defining how many seconds each experiment should run for. "He can use the joystick to go down to the different programs and if he wants to run one, then he can press the 'right' button which shows an arrow on the screen and then starts that program," says David. "The results are written to the SD card and they go into a folder called Transfer, which Tim can copy and send down to us."

Tim will be conducting experiments of his own away from the Pi. One will involve studying metals using the on-board electromagnetic levitator, a furnace which heats the metals to 2,100°C and rapidly cools them in a gravityless environment. The removal of gravity allows for a more accurate observation of fundamental properties of different metals, alloys, and the rates of cooling.

He will also be looking at organisms placed on the exterior of the ISS to see how a lack of oxygen, extreme temperature changes, and radiation affects them. Perhaps most importantly, Tim will study the measurement of brain pressure in space. There has long been a worry that space exploration (and time on the ISS) can affect the vision of astronauts. As low gravity allows blood to rise, it increases brain pressure and pushing on the back of the eyes. Tim will help researchers at the University Hospital Southampton NHS Foundation Trust better understand the open fluid links between the brain and the ear that could form a better way of testing astronaut health.

But where does that leave the education part of his mission? "In the official world, Tim will have four hours of education activity time per expedition," say Libby. With Tim working within Expedition 46 and 47, that equates to eight hours. It doesn't sound a lot and Libby admits

> "Only a small number of people can be an astronaut"

it isn't – "in space everything floats, so we usually say work out how long it will take to do something on Earth and triple the time" – but Tim is brilliantly committed to ensuring the mission is fun for the next generation of children. To that end, he wants them to get the most out of it and share the mission. "He will spend a lot of Saturday afternoons working on education projects," says Libby. "Astro Pi is one of our flagship education programmes and we're looking forward to it. Education is going to be very important in Tim's mission."

As such, this could well be a turning point for the space industry in the UK. "Only a small number of people can be an astronaut, and that is what kids think about," says David. "They also see space as abstract and only associate it with NASA. But we are showing the various roles and the possibilities. We're calling it the Tim Peake effect and we hope that in five to ten years' time we have a booming space industry [similar to the Apollo effect in the USA in the 1960s and 1970s, which boosted interest in science and engineering]. It's a bold aim, but it's everybody's hope."

[CHAPTER THREE]

GET STARTED WITH THE SENSE HAT

Now you know all about the Sense HAT and its part in Astro Pi, it's time to learn how you can actually use one for your own stellar projects

You'll Need

- Sense HAT magpi.cc/SenseHAT
- Sense HAT Python library magpi.cc/1RKRoqc (pre-installed on Raspbian Jessie)

You don't need to be in space to make use of the Sense HAT: it works down on Earth as well! Once you've managed to get your hands on one, you'll probably want to start using it, which is where this chapter comes in handy. You can find out more about what the Sense HAT can do by following the Astro Pi Guide (**magpi.cc/AstroPiGuide**), which will show you how to connect and test your Sense HAT. It also has some helpful explanations and examples of what the different inputs and outputs can do.

In order to write your programs, though, you'll need to boot your Raspberry Pi to the desktop and start IDLE3, the Python 3 editor, by entering the following command into a Terminal window:

```
sudo idle3 &
```

For our first trick, we'll display text on the HAT's LED matrix. This program contains two crucial lines of code, which import the Sense HAT software and create a **sense** object which represents the Sense HAT:

```
from sense_hat import SenseHat

sense = SenseHat()
```

The next line makes the Sense HAT actually do something:

```
sense.show_message(
"I want to be an astronaut!")
```

You've probably already discovered that you can easily change the message to your own text, but there's much more you can do. For example, we can expand the **sense.show_message** command to include some extra parameters which will change the behaviour of the message – see **Fig 1** on the following page for details.

The following program will display the text "Astro Pi is awesome!" more slowly, with the text in yellow **[255,255,0]** and the background in blue **[0,0,255]**:

```
from sense_hat import SenseHat

sense = SenseHat()

sense.show_message("Astro Pi is awesome!",
scroll_speed=0.05, text_colour=[255,255,0], back_
colour=[0,0,255])
```

You could also make the message repeat by using a **while** loop:

```
from sense_hat import SenseHat
sense = SenseHat()
while True:
    sense.show_message(
"Astro Pi is awesome!!", scroll_speed=0.05, text_colour=
[255,255,0], back_colour=[0,0,255])
```

Now we've made our first program, we should save it. Click **File > Save As**, give your program a name like **loop_text.py,** then press **F5** to run it. Easy!

The LED matrix can also display a single character rather than an entire message, using the **sense.show_letter** function, which has the same optional parameters (see **Fig 1**).

Fig 1 Available parameters for the **show_message** command

PARAMETER	EFFECT
scroll_speed	The scroll_speed parameter affects how quickly the text moves on the screen. The default value is 0.1. The bigger the number, the slower the speed.
text_colour	The text_colour parameter alters the colour of the text and is specified as three values for red, green, and blue. Each value can be between 0 and 255, so [255,0,255] would be red + blue = purple.
back_colour	The back_colour parameter alters the colour of the background and is specified as three values for red, green, and blue. Each value can be between 0 and 255, so [255,255,0] would be red + green = yellow.

Displaying images

Of course, the LED matrix can display more than just text. We can control each LED individually to create our own images, and there are a couple of different ways we can accomplish this. The first approach is to set pixels (LEDs) individually; we can do this using the **sense.set_pixel()** command. First, we need to be clear about how we describe each pixel.

The Sense HAT uses a coordinate system; the numbering begins at 0, not 1. The origin is in the top-left rather than the bottom-left, as you may be used to. Try the following program (and see **Fig 2**):

```
from sense_hat import SenseHat
sense = SenseHat()
sense.set_pixel(0, 2, [0, 0, 255])
sense.set_pixel(7, 4, [255, 0, 0])
```

Setting pixels individually works, but it gets rather complex when you want to set lots of pixels. There is another option, though: **sense.set_pixels**.

This is quite straightforward; we just give a list of colour values for each pixel. We could enter:

```
sense.set_pixels([[255, 0, 0],
[255, 0, 0], [255, 0, 0], [255, 0, 0],...])
```

...but this would take ages. Instead, you can use some variables to define your colour palette. In this example we're using the colours of the rainbow:

```
r = [255, 0, 0]
o = [255, 127, 0]
y = [255, 255, 0]
g = [0, 255, 0]
b = [0, 0, 255]
i = [75, 0, 130]
v = [159, 0, 255]
e = [0, 0, 0]  # e is for empty
```

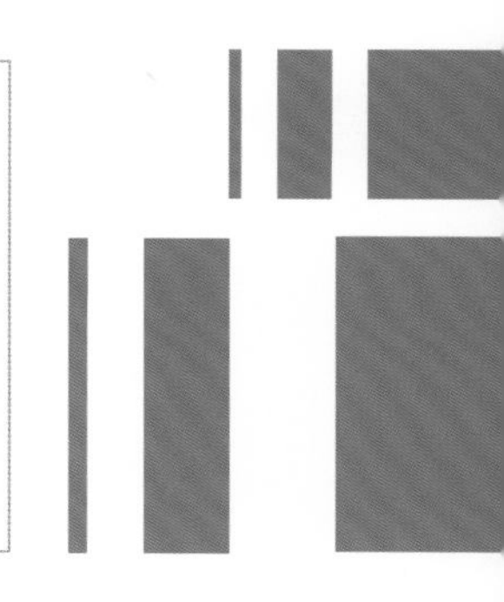

We can then describe our matrix by creating a 2D list of colour names:

```
image = [ e,e,e,e,e,e,e,e,
          e,e,e,r,r,e,e,e,
          e,r,r,o,o,r,r,e,
          r,o,o,y,y,o,o,r,
          o,y,y,g,g,y,y,o,
          y,g,g,b,b,g,g,y,
          b,b,b,i,i,b,b,b,
          b,i,i,v,v,i,i,b ]
```

Once you have the colour and image variables, you can then simply call them by adding:

`sense.set_pixels(image)`

...but don't forget to start your listing with:

```
from sense_hat import SenseHat
sense = SenseHat()
```

Click **File > Save As**, give your program a name e.g. **rainbow.py**, then press F5 to run. What will you display on your Sense HAT?

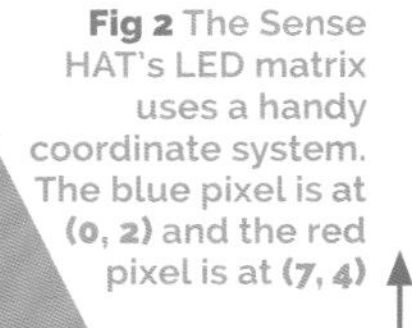

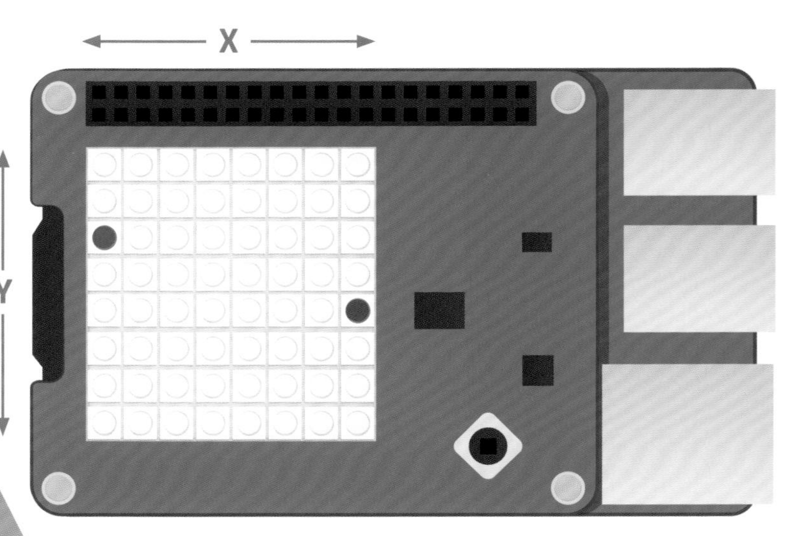

Fig 2 The Sense HAT's LED matrix uses a handy coordinate system. The blue pixel is at **(0, 2)** and the red pixel is at **(7, 4)**

Setting Orientation

So far, all our text and images have appeared the same way up, assuming that the HDMI port is at the bottom. However, this may not always be the case (especially in space) so you may want to change the orientation of the matrix. To do this, you can use the **sense.set_rotation()** method and inside the brackets enter one of four angles **(0, 90, 180, 270)**.

To rotate your screen by 180 degrees you'd use this line:

```
sense.set_rotation(180)
```

When used in the rainbow program it would look like this:

```
from sense_hat import SenseHat

sense = SenseHat()

r = [255, 0, 0]
o = [255, 127, 0]
y = [255, 255, 0]
g = [0, 255, 0]
b = [0, 0, 255]
i = [75, 0, 130]
v = [159, 0, 255]
e = [0, 0, 0]

image = [
e,e,e,e,e,e,e,e,
e,e,e,r,r,e,e,e,
e,r,r,o,o,r,r,e,
r,o,o,y,y,o,o,r,
o,y,y,g,g,y,y,o,
y,g,g,b,b,g,g,y,
b,b,b,i,i,b,b,b,
b,i,i,v,v,i,i,b
]

sense.set_pixels(image)
sense.set_rotation(180)
```

Click **File -- Save As**, give your program a name e.g. **rainbow_flip.py**, then press F5 to run.

You could also create spinning text using a for loop:

```
from sense_hat import SenseHat
import time

sense = SenseHat()

sense.show_letter("J")

angles = [0, 90, 180, 270, 0, 90, 180, 270]
for r in angles:
    sense.set_rotation(r)
    time.sleep(0.5)
```

This program displays the letter "J" and then sets the rotation to each value in the angles list with a 0.5 second pause. Click **File -- Save As**, give your program a name e.g. **spinning_j.py**, then press F5 to run.

You can also flip the image on the screen, either horizontally or vertically, using these lines:

```
sense.flip_h()
```

or

```
sense.flip_v()
```

With this example you could create a simple animation by flipping the image repeatedly:

```
from sense_hat import SenseHat
import time

sense = SenseHat()

w = [150, 150, 150]
b = [0, 0, 255]
```

```
e = [0, 0, 0]

image = [
e,e,e,e,e,e,e,e,
e,e,e,e,e,e,e,e,
w,w,w,e,e,w,w,w,
w,w,b,e,e,w,w,b,
w,w,w,e,e,w,w,w,
e,e,e,e,e,e,e,e,
e,e,e,e,e,e,e,e,
e,e,e,e,e,e,e,e
]

sense.set_pixels(image)

while True:
    time.sleep(1)
    sense.flip_h()
```

Click **File -- Save As**, give your program a name e.g. **eyes.py**, then press **F5** to run.

Sensing the environment

The Sense HAT has a set of environmental sensors for detecting the conditions around it. It can detect pressure, temperature and humidity. We can collect these readings using three simple methods:

sense.get_temperature() - this will return the temperature in Celsius.
sense.get_pressure() - this will return the pressure in millibars.
sense.get_humidity() - this will return the humidity as a percentage.

Using these, we could create a simple scrolling text display which could keep people informed about current conditions:

```
from sense_hat import SenseHat
sense = SenseHat()

while True:
```

```
        t = sense.get_temperature()
        p = sense.get_pressure()
        h = sense.get_humidity()

        t = round(t, 1)
        p = round(p, 1)
        h = round(h, 1)

        msg = "Temperature = %s, Pressure=%s, Humidity=%s" %
(t,p,h)

        sense.show_message(msg, scroll_speed=0.05)
```

Click **File -- Save As**, give your program a name e.g. **env.py**, then press F5 to run.

You could now use some colour to let the astronauts know whether conditions are within sensible ranges. According to some online documentation, the International Space Station maintains these conditions at the following levels:

Temperature (18.3 - 26.7 Celsius)
Pressure (979 - 1027 millibars)
Humidity (around 60%)

You could use an **if** statement in your code to check these conditions, and set a background colour for the scroll:

```
if t > 18.3 and t < 26.7:
    bg = [0, 100, 0] # green
else:
    bg = [100, 0, 0] # red
```

Your complete program would look like this:

```
from sense_hat import SenseHat
sense = SenseHat()

while True:
```

```
    t = sense.get_temperature()
    p = sense.get_pressure()
    h = sense.get_humidity()

    t = round(t, 1)
    p = round(p, 1)
    h = round(h, 1)

    if t > 18.3 and t < 26.7:
        bg = [0, 100, 0]  # green
    else:
        bg = [100, 0, 0]  # red

    msg = "Temperature = %s, Pressure=%s, Humidity=%s" %
(t, p, h)

    sense.show_message(msg, scroll_speed=0.05, back_
colour=bg)
```

Click **File -- Save As**, give your program a name e.g. scrolling_env.py, then press **F5** to run.

Detecting movement

The Sense HAT has a set of sensors that can detect movement. It has an IMU (inertial measurement unit) chip which includes a gyroscope for detecting which way up the board is, an accelerometer for detecting movement and a magnetometer for detecting magnetic fields.

Before you start experimenting with motion sensing, it's important to understand three key terms when we talk about the three axes of motion: pitch, roll, and yaw. Pitch is like a plane taking off or diving, roll is for spinning the plane and yaw is for steering left and right like a car. It's visualised in **Fig 3**.

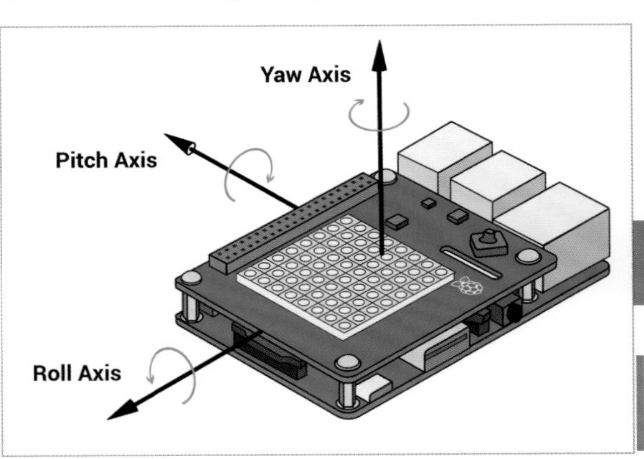

Fig 3 Roll, Pitch, and Yaw

You can find out the orientation of the Sense HAT using the sense.get_orientation() method:

```
pitch, roll, yaw = sense.get_orientation().values()
```

This would get the three orientation values (measured in degrees) and store them as the three variables pitch, roll, and yaw. The .values() obtains the three values so that they can be stored separately.

You can explore these values with a simple program:

```
from sense_hat import SenseHat

sense = SenseHat()

while True:
    pitch, roll, yaw = sense.get_orientation().values()
    print("pitch=%s, roll=%s, yaw=%s" % (pitch,yaw,roll))
```

Click File -- Save As, give your program a name e.g. orientation.py, then press F5 to run. When using the movement sensors it is important to poll them often in a tight loop. If you poll them too slowly, for example with time.sleep(0.5) in your loop, you will see strange results. This is because the code behind needs lots of measurements in order to successfully combine the data coming from the gyroscope, accelerometer and magnetometer.

Another way to detect orientation is to use the sense.get_accelerometer_raw() method which tells you the amount of g-force acting on each axis. If any axis has ±1g then you know that axis is pointing downwards.

In this example, the amount of gravitational acceleration for each axis (x, y, and z) is extracted and is then rounded to the nearest whole number:

```
from sense_hat import SenseHat

sense = SenseHat()

while True:
    x, y, z = sense.get_accelerometer_raw().values()
```

```
    x=round(x, 0)
    y=round(y, 0)
    z=round(z, 0)

    print("x=%s, y=%s, z=%s" % (x, y, z))
```

Click **File -- Save As**, give your program a name e.g. **acceleration.py**, then press **F5** to run. As you turn the screen you should see the values for x and y change between -1 and 1. If you place the Pi flat or turn it upside down, the z axis will be 1 and then -1.

If we know which way round the Raspberry Pi is, then we can use that information to set the orientation of the LED matrix. First you would display something on the matrix, then continually check which way round the board is, and use that to update the orientation of the display:

```
from sense_hat import SenseHat

sense = SenseHat()

sense.show_letter("J")

while True:
    x, y, z = sense.get_accelerometer_raw().values()

    x = round(x, 0)
    y = round(y, 0)

    if x == -1:
        sense.set_rotation(180)
    elif y == 1:
        sense.set_rotation(90)
    elif y == -1:
        sense.set_rotation(270)
    else:
        sense.set_rotation(0)
```

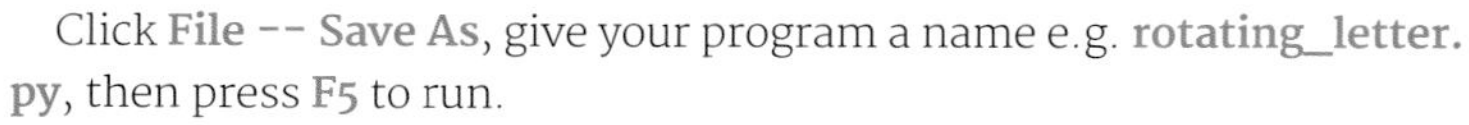

Click **File -- Save As**, give your program a name e.g. **rotating_letter.py**, then press **F5** to run.

In this program you are using an **if, elif, else** structure to check which way round the Raspberry Pi is. The **if** and **elif** test three of the orientations, and if the orientation doesn't match any of these then the program assumes it is the "right" way round. By using the **else** statement we also catch all those other situations, like when the board is at 45 degrees or sitting level.

If the board is only rotated, it will only experience 1g of acceleration in any direction; if we were to shake it, the sensor would experience more than 1g. We could then detect that rapid motion and respond. For this program we will introduce the **abs()** function, which is not specific to the Sense HAT library and is part of standard Python. **abs()** gives us the size of a value and ignores whether the value is positive or negative. This is helpful as we don't care which direction the sensor is being shaken, just that it is shaken:

```
from sense_hat import SenseHat

sense = SenseHat()

while True:
    x, y, z = sense.get_accelerometer_raw().values()

    x = abs(x)
    y = abs(y)
    z = abs(z)

    if x > 1 or y > 1 or z > 1:
        sense.show_letter("!", text_colour=[255, 0, 0])
    else:
        sense.clear()
```

Click **File -- Save As**, give your program a name e.g. **shake.py**, then press **F5** to run. You might find this is quite sensitive, but you could change the value from 1 to a higher number.

We've now covered every function that the Sense HAT is capable of – now bring it all together for one incredible project!

[CHAPTER FOUR]

GRAVITY SIMULATOR

The strength of gravity isn't always the same: here's how to simulate the way it changes for a cat with a simple program on your Raspberry Pi

You'll Need

- Raspbian **magpi.cc/1MYYTMo**
- Scratch (pre-installed on Raspbian)

In space, it feels as if everything is floating. This is because everything becomes weightless outside of our planet, Earth. This is probably the biggest difference astronauts experience in space, compared to being on Earth, where everything is pulled down towards the ground. On Earth we can all feel this downward pull, but we are so used to it that we sometimes don't even think about it. This pull or attraction we feel is called gravity.

You can recreate the effects of the force of gravity on Earth in this Scratch simulation.

Open Scratch by clicking on **Menu** and **Programming**, followed by **Scratch**. Alternatively, you can use Scratch 2.0 online for this activity, although be aware that some of the blocks may be slightly different. Create a new file by selecting **File** and **New**.

Next, delete the Scratch cat sprite by right-clicking on it and selecting **Delete** from the menu that is displayed. For this project, you need to create a new background to act as the Earth. To do this, click on **Stage** in the sprites palette (bottom-right) and then click on **Backgrounds** next to the **Scripts** tab. Click on **Paint** to draw your own background, then select the rectangle icon and a green colour. It is important that you fill the rectangle with one solid colour.

FIG 01

```
when [flag] clicked
go to x: 0 y 148
set gravity to -9.81
set velocity to 0
forever
    change velocity by (gravity * 0.1)
    change y by velocity
```

Draw a green rectangle at the bottom of the image to represent the Earth. Once you're happy with your stage design, click **OK**.

You'll need to choose a sprite to use as your character. You can use the Scratch cat sprite, or you can use our Mooncake the Astro Cat sprite. You can find Mooncake here: **magpi.cc/1PEbjIm**. Once you've got it, add it as a new sprite by clicking on the middle icon on the sprites palette, selecting **Astro-cat.png** from the choices and clicking **OK**.

In order for your gravity simulator to work with this sprite, you'll need to **set the costume center** of Mooncake the Astro Cat by selecting the sprite, then clicking on **Costumes** followed by **Edit**. In the Paint Editor window, you'll see a button with a '+' symbol on it. When clicked, it will show a crosshair over the sprite, which you'll be able to move with your mouse. Move it so that it selects Mooncake's tummy and, when you are happy, click **OK**.

Click on the **Scripts** tab of the sprite and save your Scratch project work by clicking on **File** and **Save As**. Name your program **Gravity simulation** and save it in your home directory or some place that you can find it later.

Storing data

To create a variable, click on **Variables** in the blocks palette (top-left) and then click **Make a Variable**. The New Variable window opens and asks you to type a name for your variable. Name the first variable `gravity` and ensure that **For all sprites** is checked before clicking **OK**. A variable holds a value that can be changed, and can be used elsewhere in your program.

You'll see some orange blocks are added to your **Variables** area, called `gravity`, and a small counter box will appear on the stage. You'll also need to make another variable in the same way as you've just done, called `velocity`.

FIG 02

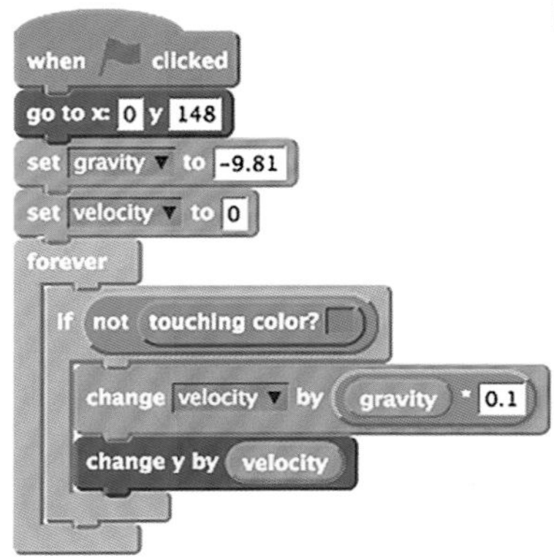

```
when [flag] clicked
go to x: 0 y: 148
set gravity to -9.81
set velocity to 0
forever
  if not touching color? [ ]
    change velocity by (gravity * 0.1)
    change y by velocity
```

FIG 03

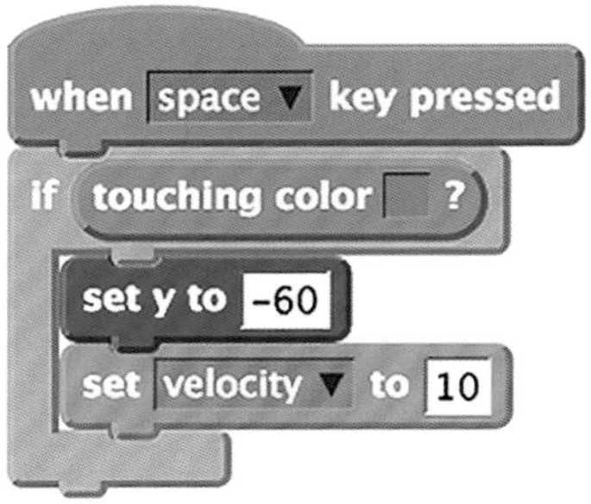

```
when space key pressed
if touching color [ ] ?
  set y to -60
  set velocity to 10
```

Now we have variables, you can start to build up the script. Return to the **Scripts** tab, then click on **Control** in the blocks palette. Begin by dragging a **when green flag clicked** block into the main script area.

To make sure that Mooncake starts at the top of the screen at the start of the program, you'll need to set the coordinates. Use a **go to x: 0 y: 0** block from the **Motion** blocks area. Drag it over and clip it beneath **when green flag clicked**, then enter **x** as **0** and **y** as **148**.

Next, you will need to store some data inside your variable blocks. To do this, use a **set gravity to 0** block from the **Variables** area and replace the value with **-9.81**, which is the calculation of the force of gravity on Earth. Similarly, set the **velocity** variable to **0**.

The simulation loop

In this program you want to change the velocity variable to simulate how gravity works. In physics, there are lots of mathematical equations that we use to calculate different forces, including gravity. To change the velocity variable you can use the following calculation:

```
Velocity = Gravity × Timestep
Velocity = -9.81   × 0.1
```

The value **0.1** is a time step in this program, so that each time around the loop it will be multiplied by **gravity** (which is -9.81) and output the velocity.

> "The program so far simulates gravity by dropping Mooncake from the top of the screen..."

Dock a **forever** block from the **Control** section beneath your **set velocity** block and place a **change velocity by 0** **Variables** block inside the **forever** loop. Next, take a multiplier Operators block (**0 * 0**) and place it inside the space at the end of the **change velocity by** block. Drag the **gravity** variable and place it in the right side of the multiplication operator, and then type **0.1** in the other.

The last block needed is a Motion block to move the Mooncake sprite. Use the **change y by** motion block and add it into the loop, then drag the **velocity** variable and add it into the white space in the **change y by** block. The script should look like **Fig 01**. Save your program and click the green flag to check that it works.

The program so far simulates gravity by dropping Mooncake from the top of the screen to the bottom, but you will notice that she isn't landing on the carefully drawn Earth. You can change this by adding a conditional statement inside the simulation loop.

Select the **Control** blocks area and drag an **if** block onto the scripts area. Place it inside the **forever** loop, wrapping around the **set velocity** and **change y by** blocks. Next, set your condition to the **if** block using a **not** operator block, which should be placed into the diamond shape next to the word **if**. Then take the **touching color?** block from the **Sensing** area and place it into the space in the **not** operator block.

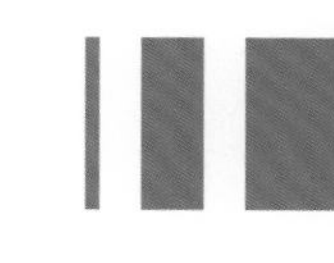

The colour shown in the **touching color** block needs to match the Stage background green colour of Earth. To match them exactly, click on the coloured box inside **touching color** and the mouse pointer will transform into a little eye-dropper icon. Move your mouse onto the Earth in the Scratch preview window and click on the green colour. The block will change to display the same colour. Your blocks should look like they do in **Fig 02**. Save your program and click the green flag to see if Mooncake will land on the Earth.

Try to figure out how you can make Mooncake jump when she's on the planet, using the space bar! We'll give you a hint: look at **Fig 03**...

The MagPi ESSENTIALS

[CHAPTER FIVE]

MAKE A DIGITAL MAGIC 8 BALL

Bring the time-honoured tradition of shaken-not-stirred fortunes to the Sense HAT, making use of those motion sensors

You'll Need

- Sense HAT **magpi.cc/SenseHAT**
- Sense HAT Python library **magpi.cc/1RKRoqc** (pre-installed with Raspbian Jessie)

In this activity you will build your own Magic 8 Ball using your Raspberry Pi, a Sense HAT, and some Python code. A Magic 8 Ball is a toy to which you verbally ask a closed question. You then shake it, and it will give you a prediction.

In this tutorial you will use IDLE 3, the Python development environment, to write some code for the Sense HAT. This means you can test your code and fix it as you write it. To open IDLE 3, click on the main Raspbian **Menu** (top-left), followed by **Programming** and then **Python 3 (IDLE)**.

Once the Python shell window has loaded, click on **File** and **New File**. This will open a text editor window in which you can write, save and test your code. Save the blank file as **magic8ball.py** by clicking on **File** and **Save As.**

Printing replies to the screen

A good way to start your Magic 8 Ball program is first to create a text version of how it works. Let's think about what a Magic 8 Ball does. First, you ask it a question, before shaking the ball, turning it over, and then reading a reply that it has randomly selected. You will therefore need a list of replies and a way of randomly choosing one from the list and displaying that answer on the screen.

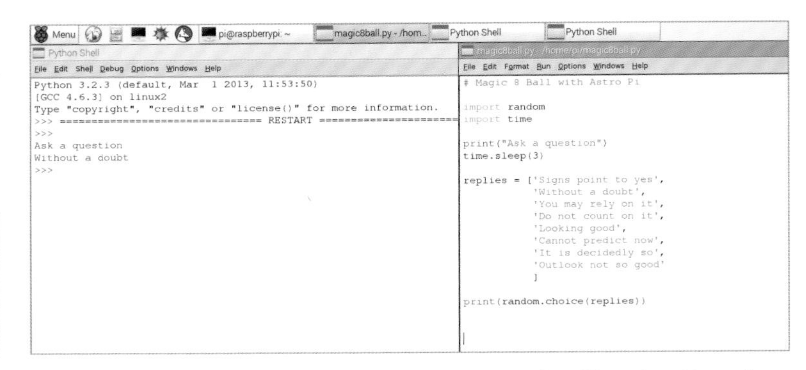

Fig 1 Test the program first in a Python shell window

To start, you need to import the **random** and **time** libraries. Type the following into your **magic8ball.py** text file:

```
import random
import time
```

Using the **print** function, you can print text to the screen for the person using your program. Type:

```
print("Ask a question")
```

Then there needs to be a pause before the program responds, so that the user can ask a question verbally or mentally. You can use the **time** library to ask the program to sleep for a set amount of time, like this:

```
time.sleep(3)
```

The program will pause for three seconds. You can change this sleep value to make the pause longer or shorter. Now, create a list of replies that the program could give to the question. Lists can be named in much the same way as variables; for example, `number = [1, 2, 3, 4]`. This list called 'number' has four items in it. Your list will contain strings of text that will be displayed on the screen; these strings will be quite long. To create your list, type:

```
replies = ['Signs point to yes', 'Without a doubt',
'You may rely on it']
```

Add as many replies to your list as you like. Make sure that you separate each reply with a comma. You can break up your list onto multiple lines, like this, to make it easier to read; however, this is not required for your program to work:

```
replies = ['Signs point to yes',
        'Without a doubt',
        'You may rely on it',
        'Do not count on it',
        'Looking good',
        'Cannot predict now',
        'It is decidedly so',
        'Outlook not so good'
        ]
```

Finally, an instruction is needed to select an item from the list at random and then display it on the screen. You can use the **random** library to do this, by typing:

```
print(random.choice(replies))
```

Save your code by clicking on **File** and **Save**, then run your program to test it works by clicking on **Run** and **Run Module**. Your code should look similar to that in **Fig 1**.

Display text on the Sense HAT

Now that you have text outputting to the Python 3 shell window on your screen, let's change the code so that the text scrolls across the LED matrix on your Sense HAT. To do this, you will need to use the **SenseHat** library and replace the print functions with a 'show message' function. Underneath the import modules section of your code, add the following lines:

Fig 2 You can alter the speed of the scrolling text

```
magic8ball1.py - /home/pi/magic8ball1.py
File Edit Format Run Options Windows Help
# Magic 8 Ball

import random
import time
from sense_hat import SenseHat

sh = SenseHat()

sh.show_message("Ask a question", scroll_speed=(0.06))
time.sleep(3)

replies = ['Signs point to yes',
           'Without a doubt',
           'You may rely on it',
           'Do not count on it',
           'Looking good',
           'Cannot predict now',
           'It is decidedly so',
           'Outlook not so good'
           ]

sh.show_message(random.choice(replies), scroll_speed=(0.06))
```

```
from sense_hat import SenseHat
sh = SenseHat()
```

Next, replace **print** with **sh.show_message** in your code. There are two places where you will need to do this. To test the code, save your program by pressing CTRL+S on your keyboard, then run it by pressing F5 to check that it works on the Sense HAT.

You may find that the text is slow to scroll across the LED matrix on your Sense HAT. To speed up the text, you can add **scroll_speed=(0.06)** to your text strings, as in Fig 2.

Normal Magic 8 Balls work by being shaken up after asking a question. How do you think you could make that happen using the Sense HAT's motion sensors? That's your next programming challenge!

Right A little hint for how to use the Sense HAT's motion sensors so you can shake your Magic 8 Ball

magic8ball2.py - /home/pi/magic8ball2.py

File Edit Format Run Options Windows Help

```
# Magic 8 Ball

import random
import time
from sense_hat import SenseHat

sh = SenseHat()

sh.show_message("Ask a question & shake", scroll_speed=(0.06))
time.sleep(3)

replies = ['Signs point to yes',
           'Without a doubt',
           'You may rely on it',
           'Do not count on it',
           'Looking good',
           'Cannot predict now',
           'It is decidedly so',
           'Outlook not so good'
           ]

while True:
    x, y, z = sh.get_accelerometer_raw().values()

    x = abs(x)
    y = abs(y)
    z = abs(z)

    if x > 2 or y > 2 or z > 2 :
        sh.show_message(random.choice(replies), scroll_speed=(0.06))
    else:
        sh.clear()
```

Ln: 34 Col: 0

[CHAPTER SIX]
INTERACTIVE PIXEL PET

Create a pint-sized pocket monster living in the digital world of a Raspberry Pi Sense HAT

You'll Need

- Sense HAT **magpi.cc/SenseHAT**
- Sense HAT Python library **magpi.cc/1RKRoqc** (pre-installed with Raspbian Jessie)
- Pypng **magpi.cc/1lj5ijm**
- 8×8GridDraw **magpi.cc/1lj5oYo**

Using sensors and output devices is a great way to make your computer programs more interactive. The Raspberry Pi Sense HAT contains a whole set of sensors that can be used to detect movement, which will be used in this activity to take a digital pet for a walk.

The first thing that needs to be done is to install the extra software required for this tutorial. Install the Python PNG library – an image library for Python that uses the PNG file type – by opening a Terminal with **Menu**, **Accessories**, **Terminal**, and typing:

```
sudo pip3 install pypng
```

Press **ENTER**. After that has been installed, remain in the Terminal and type:

```
git clone https://github.com/jrobinson-uk/
RPi_8x8GridDraw
```

You'll need to design your pet avatar before you program any actions.

There are examples of some famous characters you can make on an excellent sprite sheet created by Johan Vinet, which can be found at **magpi.cc/1SrqGDm**.

Open a Terminal by clicking on **Menu**, **Accessories**, and **Terminal**. Enter the line **`cd RPi_8x8GridDraw`**, followed by **`python3 sense_grid.py`**. This will run an application which you can use to draw your space pet avatar, as seen in **Fig 1** on page 47.

Simply select the colour you wish to use from the grid with your mouse pointer, and then select the circle in the grid to change it to that colour.

Alternatively, you may wish to draw your picture out on squared paper with coloured pencils. You'll need two pet designs, with the second preferably very similar to the first, so that we can animate your pet. In **Fig 2** on page 48, you can see that our two images are almost identical to each other, but the feet are in a different place.

Later, when you code your animation, you will create the illusion that the pet is walking.

Labelling each pixel

Think of a letter from the alphabet to represent each colour in your pixel pet image, for example, **w** for white or **r** for red. If using squared paper for your design, you can write the letters on top: see **Fig 3** below. Note that **e** stands for **empty**.

If you're using the 8x8GridDraw editor, then you can write out your squares on paper, representing each colour with a letter and separating them with a comma. Alternatively, you could type them into a text editor like Leafpad, which you can find by clicking on **Menu**, **Accessories**, and **Text Editor**. You'll end up with something that looks like this:

```
e, e, e, e, e, e, e, e,
p, e, e, e, e, e, e, e,
e, p, e, e, p, e, p, e,
e, p, g, g, p, y, y, e,
e, g, g, g, y, w, y, g,
e, g, g, g, g, y, y, e,
e, g, e, g, e, g, e, e,
e, e, e, e, e, e, e, e
```

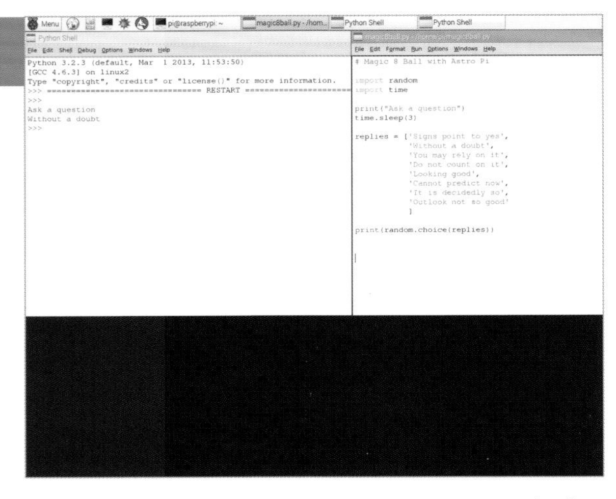

Fig 1 Using 8×8GridDraw

You'll notice that we have eight rows and eight columns of letters, each separated by a comma, to make up the LED matrix on the Sense HAT. Repeat this step for your second pet design, so that you end up with two grids of letters. Can you think of any problems that might arise when only using one letter to label different colours? How might you solve this issue?

Code your pet

Now that you have your designs represented as letters in a grid or array, you can start to code them in Python. Click on **Menu** then **Programming**, followed by **Python 3**. This will open the Python 3 shell window. Next, click on **File** and **New File** to open an empty text editor window. Save this empty file as **space-pet.py**.

First, you'll need to import all the modules and libraries required for this project in your code, by typing:

```
from sense_hat import SenseHat
import time
```

Underneath that, type:

```
sense = SenseHat()
```

Note that capital letters, full stops, and commas are very important in Python. Your code might not work if you don't include these. Next, create a **variable** for each colour label in your pet design, like this:

```
p = (204, 0, 204) # Pink
g = (0, 102, 102) # Dark Green
w = (200, 200, 200) # White
y = (204, 204, 0) # Yellow
e = (0, 0, 0) # Empty
```

The numbers used here inside the brackets are **RGB** values, or **Red**, **Green**, and **Blue** values. Mixtures of these primary colours make different shades. The higher the number, the more of that colour it will contain. For example, (255, 0, 0) would make a solid red, whereas (0, 255, 0) would create a vivid green. You can change these numbers in your code to get the colours that you want.

Next, use a **list** to store your pixel pet design, like this:

```
pet1 = [
    e, e, e, e, e, e, e, e,
    p, e, e, e, e, e, e, e,
    e, p, e, e, p, e, p, e,
    e, p, g, g, p, y, y, e,
    e, g, g, g, y, w, y, g,
    e, g, g, g, g, y, y, e,
    e, g, e, g, e, g, e, e,
    e, e, e, e, e, e, e, e
    ]
```

Here you have created a variable called **pet1** and stored a list of labels for each colour by using **[** at the start of each letter and **]** at the end. Repeat for the second pixel pet design, using a different variable name like **pet2**. Your code should start looking something like Fig 4.

Fig 2 Two very simple frames can give you enough variation to create an animation, even if the difference is a few pixels!

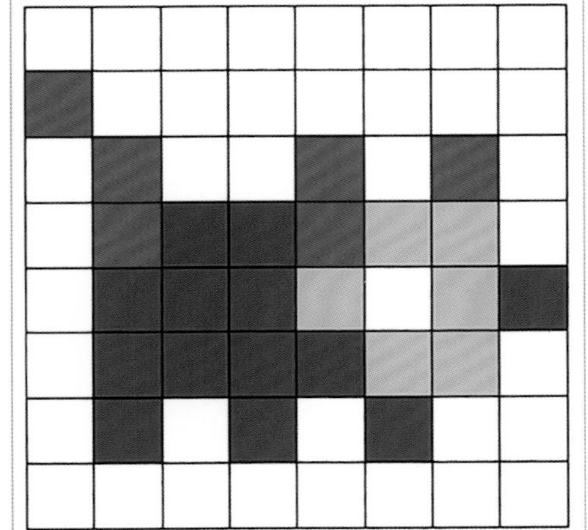

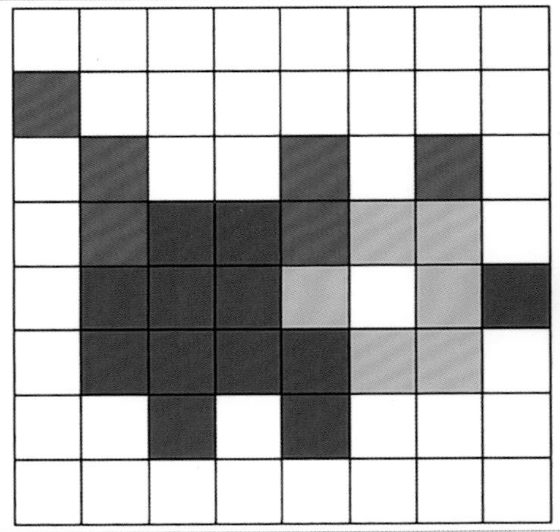

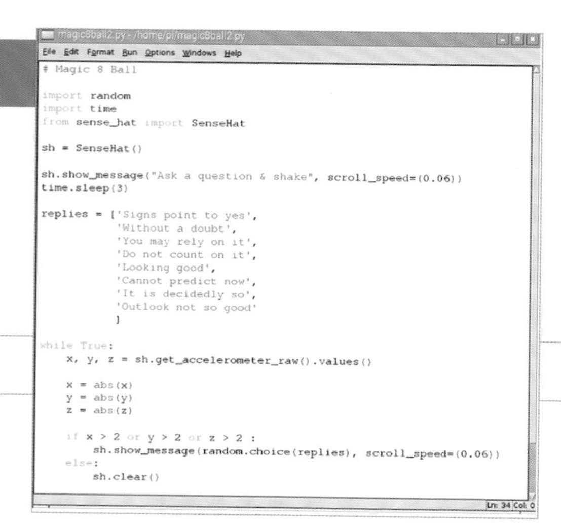

Fig 3 Thinking of the colours as letters instead of numbers makes it slightly easier to understand and code it into the program

If you ran your code now, nothing would happen, because so far you have only told the program to store information. To make something happen, you will need to write a command to call on that data and display your colours in the correct order on the Sense HAT's LED matrix. Type this command underneath your lists:

```
sense.set_pixels(pet1)
```

Save your code by pressing CTRL+S on the keyboard, followed by F5. Note what happens. Why did only one of your pet designs display? It's because you have only called **pet1** in your command.

Add a delay using the **time.sleep** function, and then call the second picture using the same command as before, like this:

```
time.sleep(0.5)
sense.set_pixels(pet2)
```

Save and run your code to see your pet.

Animate your pet

So far, your pixel pet only changes once. To animate it fully, you will need to switch repeatedly between the pictures with a time delay. You could write the commands out over and over again, but it makes more sense to put them into a loop.

Move to the end of your program and locate the **sense.set_pixels(pet1)** part. Change it to look like this:

```
for i in range(10):
    sense.set_pixels(pet1)
    time.sleep(0.5)
    sense.set_pixels(pet2)
    time.sleep(0.5)
```

space-pet.py - /home/pi/space-pet.py (3.4.2)

File Edit Format Run Options Windows Help

```
from sense_hat import SenseHat
import time

sense = SenseHat()

p = (204, 0, 204) # Pink
g = (0, 102, 102) # Gray
w = (200, 200, 200) # White
y = (204, 204, 0) # Yellow
e = (0, 0, 0) # Empty

pet1 = [
    e, e, e, e, e, e, e, e,
    p, e, e, e, e, e, e, e,
    e, p, e, e, p, e, p, e,
    e, p, g, g, p, y, y, e,
    e, g, g, g, y, w, y, g,
    e, g, g, g, g, y, y, e,
    e, g, e, g, e, g, e, e,
    e, e, e, e, e, e, e, e
    ]
```

Fig 4 At this point, your code should look a bit like this

Don't forget to add the extra **time.sleep(0.5)** on the last line, and remember to indent the lines after **for i in range(10):** as this means they are inside the **for** loop. This **for** loop with the **range** function will repeat the indented code ten times and then stop.

Save and run your code to watch the animation.You will notice that after the animation has completed, you are left with the same image still displayed on the LED matrix. There is a great function that you can use that will clear the LEDs. Add this line above your new loop to clear the LEDs when you first run your program:

```
sense.clear()
```

Create a walking function

A **function** is a piece of code that you can use over and over. As the goal is to trigger the walking animation later on, it makes sense for us to put the animation code into a function that can be called when an action has been sensed by the hardware.

To put your code into a function, you simply need to add this line above your **for** loop and indent the lines beneath, like this:

```
def walking():
    for i in range(10):
        sense.set_pixels(pet1)
        time.sleep(0.5)
        sense.set_pixels(pet2)
        time.sleep(0.5)
```

The use of **def** here means that you are **defining** a function which you have called **walking**.

Now you need to call the function. So, at the bottom of your code, type:

```
walking()
```

Shake for more

It's time to use the Sense HAT's movement sensors, in particular its **accelerometer**, to trigger the walking function to make the project more interactive. Underneath your walking function, but above the function call line of **walking()**, type:

```
x, y, z = sense.get_accelerometer_raw.values()

while x<2 and y<2 and z<2:
    x, y, z = sense.get_accelerometer_raw.values()

walking()
```

The first line will obtain current movement readings from the Sense HAT on its x, y, and z coordinates. As your Raspberry Pi is presumably sitting still on a desk, those readings will have a very low value.

A **while** loop is then introduced to continually check the accelerometer values, to see if they have changed to above or equal to the value **2**. You can help the Sense HAT have an accelerometer reading of above **2** by shaking it! Save your code and then run it. Nothing should happen until you shake your Raspberry Pi.

Space-Pet.py

Download
magpi.cc
/1mcpSli

```
from sense_hat import SenseHat
import time

sense = SenseHat()

p = (204, 0, 204) # Pink
g = (0, 102, 102) # Gray
w = (200, 200, 200) # White
y = (204, 204, 0) # Yellow
e = (0, 0, 0) # Empty

pet1 = [
    e, e, e, e, e, e, e, e,
    p, e, e, e, e, e, e, e,
    e, p, e, e, p, e, p, e,
    e, p, g, g, p, w, w, e,
    e, g, g, g, w, y, w, y,
    e, g, g, g, g, w, w, e,
    e, g, e, g, e, g, e, e,
    e, e, e, e, e, e, e, e
    ]

pet2 = [
    e, e, e, e, e, e, e, e,
    p, e, e, e, e, e, e, e,
    e, p, e, e, p, e, p, e,
    e, p, g, g, p, w, w, e,
    e, g, g, g, w, y, w, y,
    e, g, g, g, g, w, w, e,
    e, e, g, e, g, e, e, e,
    e, e, e, e, e, e, e, e
    ]

sense.clear(0, 0, 0)
x, y, z = sense.get_accelerometer_raw().values()

def walking():
    for i in range(10):
        sense.set_pixels(pet1)
        time.sleep(0.5)
        sense.set_pixels(pet2)
        time.sleep(0.5)

while x<2 and y<2 and z<2:
    x, y, z = sense.get_accelerometer_raw().values()

walking()
```

The MagPi ESSENTIALS

[CHAPTER SEVEN]

ASTRONAUT REACTION TIMES GAME

Test your reactions with this Scratch game which simulates how fast you'll need to be if you want to become an astronaut.

You'll Need

- Raspbian **magpi.cc/1MYYTMo**
- Scratch (pre-installed on Raspbian)

Things happen quickly when you're travelling at 16,000 miles per hour (around 7,000 metres per second), and when debris and micrometeoroids are heading towards you at around 22,500 miles per hour. Quick reactions and a steady hand are also needed for tasks requiring fine motor skills, such as controlling robotic arms. Astronauts are trained intensively to speed up their reactions to incidents, and to prepare them for all eventualities.

NASA scientists have conducted experiments to test astronaut reaction times. Astronauts were first assessed using a computer system on the ground, then again when they were on board the ISS, and once more when they returned. It was found that their reaction times more than doubled in space. Scientists suggest that stress, as well as the brain having to adapt to microgravity, could be the cause. Normal performance was restored soon after returning to Earth.

Let's create a game in Scratch to test your reaction skills, and those of your friends and family, to see if you could become an astronaut like Tim Peake.

You can open Scratch by clicking on **Menu** and **Programming**, followed by **Scratch**. Alternatively, you can use Scratch 2.0 online for this activity, although some of the blocks may be slightly different.

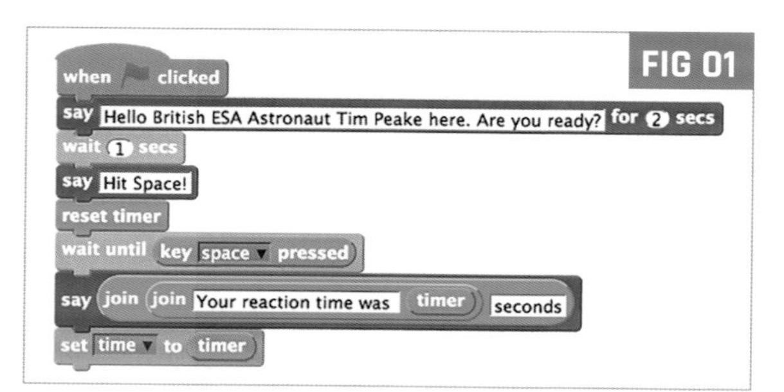

Once Scratch is open, create a new file by selecting **File** and **New**. Delete the Scratch Cat sprite by right-clicking on it and selecting **Delete** from the menu that is displayed.

For this project, you need a space-themed background and an astronaut sprite. To add a background in Scratch, click on **Stage** in the sprites palette and then click on **Backgrounds** next to the **Scripts** tab.

Click on **Paint** to draw your own background, or **Import** to use the same images as this resource. Connect your Raspberry Pi to the internet and you can download a space background (**magpi.cc/1MYZBcx**) and Tim Peake astronaut sprite (**magpi.cc/1MYZDRs**). Save them somewhere that you will be able to find them on your Raspberry Pi.

Next, add a new sprite by clicking on the **import a new sprite** icon on the sprites palette (which looks like a star coming out of a folder), selecting **Astronaut-Tim** from the choices and clicking **OK**.

Save your Scratch project work by clicking on **File** and **Save As**. Name your program **Astronaut Reaction Game** and save it in your home directory or some place that you can find it later.

Begin the game script

First, click on your Astronaut-Tim sprite to select it in the sprites palette. Select the **when green flag clicked** **Control** block from the blocks palette and place it onto the scripts area, then click on **Looks** and connect the **say for 2 secs** block to the first control block on the scripts area. Amend the text to say: 'Hello! British ESA Astronaut Tim Peake here. Are you ready?'. Add a **wait 1 secs** **Control** block underneath and then connect another **say** block and change the text for it to 'Hit Space!'.

Next, click on **Sensing** and connect the **reset timer** block. This will set the timer to 0 so that you will get an accurate measurement of how long it takes for someone to hit the space bar. Use the **Control** block **wait until** and place a **key space pressed** **Sensing** block inside the white space of the **wait until** block. This will pause the program until the player presses the space bar.

Connect another **say** block. Once the space bar has been pressed, you want to display the reaction time to the player. To do this, you need to place an Operators block called **join hello world** inside the white space in the **say** block. Replace the word 'world' with the word 'seconds'.

You will then need to replace the word 'hello' with another **join hello world** Operators block, replacing the 'hello' text with 'Your reaction time was ', and the 'world' text with the **timer** Sensing block.

Make a new variable called **time**, then select the **set time to** Variables block and add it to the script. Place the **timer** Sensing block in the **0** space (Fig 01). Save your game and test it out by clicking the green flag. When Tim says "Hit Space!", press the space bar.

Program the distance linked to your reaction time

If you are happy with the reaction game so far and have tested that it works, then you can move onto adding to the script to compare the player's reaction time to the speed at which the ISS is travelling, to calculate how far it would travel in that time.

First, you will need to make a new variable called **distance**, in the same way you did earlier. Attach a **set distance to** Variables block to your script. Place an Operators multiply block **0*0** inside where it reads **0**. To calculate the distance travelled by the ISS, you need to take the player's reaction time, stored in the **time** variable, and multiply it by 7. This is because, on average, the ISS travels 7 kilometres per second.

Add the **time** Variables block into the right-hand side of the multiplying operator and type **7** in the other side, so the whole block reads **set distance to time * 7**. Next, add a **wait 4 seconds** Control block. Add a **say** block. As in the previous step, place a **join hello world** block inside. Replace 'world' with 'kilometres'. Insert another **join hello world** block to replace 'hello'. Replace the 'hello' text in this new join block with the text 'In that time the ISS travels around '. Then replace 'world' with a **round** Operators block and fill the white space with the **distance** Variables block, as in Fig 02. Finally, save your game and test that it works by clicking on the green flag.

FIG 02

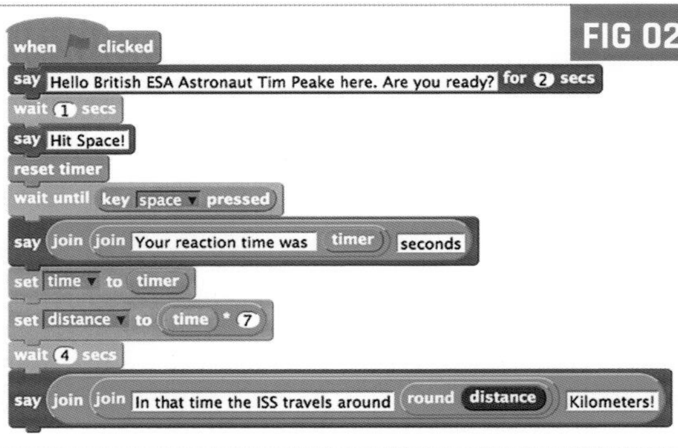

```
when [flag] clicked
say [Hello British ESA Astronaut Tim Peake here. Are you ready?] for (2) secs
wait (1) secs
say [Hit Space!]
reset timer
wait until <key [space] pressed>
say (join (join [Your reaction time was ] (timer)) [seconds])
set [time] to (timer)
set [distance] to ((time) * (7))
wait (4) secs
say (join (join [In that time the ISS travels around] (round (distance))) [Kilometers!])
```

The MagPi ESSENTIALS

[CHAPTER EIGHT]

SENSE HAT DATA LOGGER

Use your Sense HAT to take environmental readings, so you can walk around the house saying "sensors indicate..."

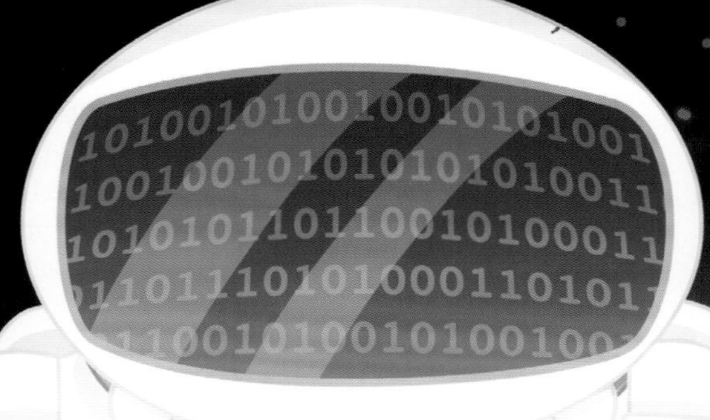

Download
magpi.cc/1M4UQXR

You'll Need

- Sense HAT **magpi.cc/SenseHAT**
- Sense HAT Python library **magpi.cc/1RKRoqc** (pre-installed with Raspbian Jessie)
- Python 3 Pillow **magpi.cc/1Srsr3C**
- Python 3 Evdev **magpi.cc/1Srsso7**

During the Astro Pi mission, a pair of Raspberry Pis with Sense HATs attached will be capturing and logging a range of data about life on board the International Space Station.

In this activity you will use a Raspberry Pi, a Sense HAT, and some Python code to create your own data-logging tool, which you can use to capture interesting data and perform experiments.

Before we start, we need to install the relevant software. Open a Terminal by going to **Menu**, **Accessories**, and **Terminal**. Type in the following and then press **ENTER:**

```
sudo pip-3.2 install pillow
sudo pip-3.2 install evdev
```

First, we'll write a short script to get data from the Sense HAT and output it to the screen. Using the sensors, we can capture the following data:

Temperature (This can be read by two different sensors)
Humidity
Pressure
Movement (This is actually made up of twelve different sensor readings)

Fig 1 Start coding

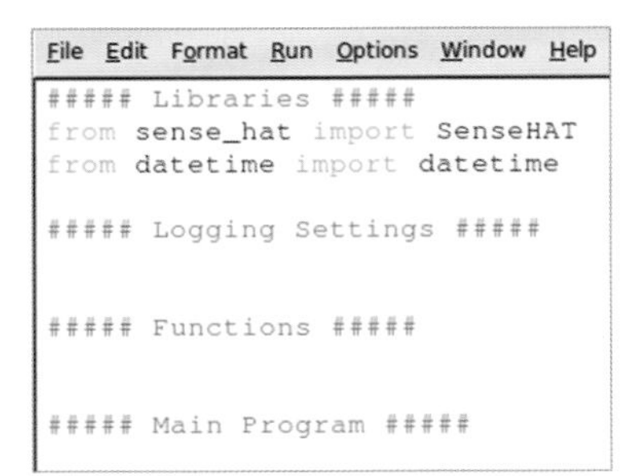

To begin your script, you need to boot your Raspberry Pi into desktop mode and run IDLE for Python 3 from the **Programming** section of the **Menu – Python 3 (IDLE)**. Once IDLE has loaded, you'll need to select **File** and then **New File**, which will load a separate window in which you can write your code.

In your blank window, add the Python code from **Fig 1**. Note that the lines starting with a **#** symbol are comments and are ignored by the computer. You use comments here to break your code into four sections, which will make it easier to build your program as it becomes more complex.

The first section, **Libraries**, is where you'll import code that will give your program extra abilities. The line **from sense_hat import SenseHat** allows your program to use the Sense HAT hardware, while the line **from datetime import datetime** allows use of time.

The section headed **Logging Settings** is where you'll be able to control different features of your logger program.

The third section, **Functions**, will contain short 'chunks' of reusable code which do a specific job, such as writing the current data to a file.

The final section, **Main Program**, is the part of your code which uses each of the functions in the correct sequence to run the whole program.

To get data from the Sense HAT, you'll need to write a function called **get_sense_data**, which will check each sensor in turn and store the sensor data in a list. The function should be added to the **Functions** section.

```
def get_sense_data():
    sense_data=[]
    sense_data.append(
sense.get_temperature_from_humidity())
    sense_data.append(
  sense.get_temperature_from_pressure())
    sense_data.append(sense.get_humidity())
    sense_data.append(sense.get_pressure())
```

The first line defines your function name. The second sets up an empty **list** structure, into which you'll add data. The next four lines obtain data from some sensors and add (or append) them to the **sense_data** list.

The rest of the sensors are a bit more complex, as they each give three values back. In the code below, you are asking the Sense HAT for each sensor's values and then extending the **sense_data** list by them.

```
o = sense.get_orientation()
yaw = o["yaw"]
pitch = o["pitch"]
roll = o["roll"]
sense_data.extend([pitch,roll,yaw])

mag = sense.get_compass_raw()
mag_x = mag["x"]
mag_y = mag["y"]
mag_z = mag["z"]
sense_data.extend([mag_x,mag_y,mag_z])

acc = sense.get_accelerometer_raw()
x = acc["x"]
y = acc["y"]
z = acc["z"]
sense_data.extend([x,y,z])

gyro = sense.get_gyroscope_raw()
gyro_x = gyro["x"]
gyro_y = gyro["y"]
gyro_z = gyro["z"]
sense_data.extend([gyro_x,gyro_y,gyro_z])

sense_data.append(datetime.now())
return sense_data
```

The current time is also appended. The final line of the function sends the **sense_data** list to where the main program will ask for it.

Next, you'll need to add the following lines to your **Main Program**

```
File  Edit  Format  Run  Options  Window  Help
##### Libraries #####
from sense_hat import SenseHAT
from datetime import datetime

##### Logging Settings #####


##### Functions #####
def get_sense_data():
    sense_data=[]

    sense_data.append(sense.get_temperature_from_humidity())
    sense_data.append(sense.get_temperature_from_pressure())
    sense_data.append(sense.get_humidity())
    sense_data.append(sense.get_pressure())

    o = sense.get_orientation()
    yaw = o["yaw"]
    pitch = o["pitch"]
    roll = o["roll"]
    sense_data.extend([pitch,roll,yaw])

    mag = sense.get_compass_raw()
    mag_x = mag["x"]
    mag_y = mag["y"]
    mag_z = mag["z"]
    sense_data.extend([mag_x,mag_y,mag_z])

    acc = sense.get_accelerometer_raw()
    x = acc["x"]
    y = acc["y"]
    z = acc["z"]
    sense_data.extend([x,y,z])

    gyro = sense.get_gyroscope_raw()
    gyro_x = gyro["x"]
    gyro_y = gyro["y"]
    gyro_z = gyro["z"]
    sense_data.extend([gyro_x,gyro_y,gyro_z])

    sense_data.append(datetime.now())

    return sense_data

##### Main Program #####
sense = SenseHat()

while True:
    sense_data = get_sense_data()
    print(sense_data)
```

Fig 2 Right now we're getting basic data from the Sense HAT, but not using it for anything

section. This will do two things: create a **sense** object, which represents the Sense HAT, and repeatedly **get_sense_data** from the sensors and display it.

```
sense = SenseHat()

while True:
    sense_data = get_sense_data()
    print(sense_data)
```

Your program should now look like **Fig 2**.

You can now test your logger. First, you should save it: press **CTRL+S** and choose a name, such as **Sense_Logger_v1.py**. Once the program is saved, you can run it by pressing **F5**. You should see lots of text scrolling past, as shown in **Fig 3** (opposite).

The highlighted section shows a single line of data bundled together into a list; you should be able to tell which sensor data is which. To stop the program running, you can press **CTRL+C** to cancel the execution.

Writing the data to file

The program you have produced so far is able to continually check the Sense HAT sensors and write this data to the screen. Unless you're a very fast reader, however, this is not very helpful.

What would be more useful would be to write this data to a CSV (comma-separated values) file, which you can examine once your logging program has finished. To create this file, you'll need to specify the file name for it, add a header row to the start of the file, convert each list of data into a line of text for the file, and periodically write a batch of data out to the file. The first thing you need to do is to add two lines to your **Settings** section. These are:

```
File Edit Shell Debug Options Windows Help
5, 4.581617897597799, 0.3486869467816896, 304.9865794244962, 61.22126388549805, 70.23302459716797, 38.42131423950195, 0.07222399860620499, 0.9874680042266846, -0.007075999863445759, -0.0005671903491020203, -0.00115656154230237, 4.08266787417233e-05, datetime.datetime(2015, 9, 23, 10, 7, 3, 613707)]
[24.833866119384766, 23.19791603088379, 58.45445251464844, 1014.267578125, 4.54403563546345, 0.3570101192547319, 304.96682310232194, 60.96324920654297, 70.86394500732422, 38.216373443603516, 0.07368800044059753, 0.9874680042266846, -0.007075999863445759, 0.0014921799302101135, 0.00019480520859360695, -0.0019599825609475374, datetime.datetime(2015, 9, 23, 10, 7, 3, 747117)]
[24.815528869628906, 23.195833206176758, 58.650001525878906, 1014.269775390625, 4.516835687754344, 0.36410756625644786, 304.95260264846996, 60.95357131958008, 70.9199447631836, 38.26530838012695, 0.07368800044059753, 0.9877119660377502, -0.00634399987757206, -0.0016143545508384705, -6.880704313516617e-05, -0.00042421312537044287, datetime.datetime(2015, 9, 23, 10, 7, 3, 873245)]
[24.87053680419922, 23.202083587646484, 58.557559967041016, 1014.26025390625, 4.485475301067053, 0.3618726536548256, 304.94150359106874, 60.84473419189453,
```

Fig 3 The raw data provided by the Sense HAT is a little tricky to understand without parsing

```
FILENAME = ""
WRITE_FREQUENCY = 50
```

The first line here will be used to choose a file name for the data output, and the second will set how often the program will write data out to the file. In this case, it will collect 50 lines of data and then add these to the file in one go.

Next, you'll need to add a **log_data** function, which will convert the **sense_data** to a line of comma-separated values ready to be written to the file. The line of text will be added to a list called **batch data**, which will store the data until it's written to the file.

Add the following code after the **Functions** heading and before the **get_sense_data** function.

```
def log_data():
  output_string = ",".join(str(value) for value in sense_data)
  batch_data.append(output_string)
```

The first line of this section takes each value in the **sense_data** list, converts them to **strings** (text), and then joins them together with the **,** symbol. Therefore, a line like this:

```
[26.7224178314209, 25.068750381469727,
53.77205276489258, 1014.18017578125, 3.8002126669234286,
306.1720338870328, 0.3019065275890227, 71.13333892822266,
59.19926834106445, 39.75812911987305, 0.9896639585494995,
0.12468399852514267, -0.004147999919950962, -0.0013064055
237919092, -0.0006561130285263062, -0.0011542239226400852,
datetime.datetime(2015, 9, 23, 11, 53, 9, 267584)]
```

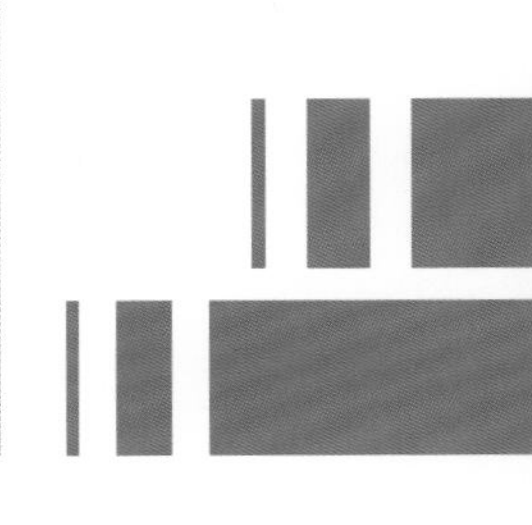

...gets converted to:

```
26.7224178314209,25.068750381469727,53.77205276489258,1014
.18017578125,3.8002126669234286,306.1720338870328,
0.3019065275890227,71.13333892822266,59.19926834106445,39.75
812911987305,0.9896639585494995,0.12468399852514267,
-0.004147999919950962,-0.0013064055237919092,
-0.0006561130285263062,-0.0011542239226400852,
2015-09-23 11:53:09.267584
```

Another function you'll need is **file_setup**, which will create a list of headings that will be written to the file before any data. This function is shown below, and needs to be added to the **Functions** section of your program.

```
def file_setup(filename):
  header  =["temp_h","temp_p","humidity","pressure",
  "pitch","roll","yaw",
  "mag_x","mag_y","mag_z",
  "accel_x","accel_y","accel_z",
  "gyro_x","gyro_y","gyro_z",
  "timestamp"]

  with open(filename,"w") as f:
      f.write(",".join(str(value) for value in header)+ "\n")
```

This function is slightly different to the previous one, as it needs an input (or **parameter**) in order to work; in this case, the input has been called **filename**. When the main program calls this function, it must also give the function the name of the file to write to. If it were called as **file_setup("output.csv")**, the function would create the file **output.csv**.

The function itself creates a list of header names, called **header**. It then opens a file in **write** mode (which will overwrite any previous data) and refers to that file as **f**. While the file is open, it joins all the list headings together using commas, and writes that line to the file.

The two functions and the settings you have added now need to be used in the main program.

Straight after the lines that read:

```
##### Main Program #####
sense = SenseHat()
```

...add the following:

```
batch_data= []

if FILENAME == "":
  filename = "SenseLog-"+str(datetime.now())+".csv"
else:
  filename = FILENAME+"-"+str(datetime.now())+".csv"

file_setup(filename)
```

The first line here creates an empty list that the program will keep adding **sense_data** lines to until it reaches 50 (or whatever value is set by **WRITE_FREQUENCY**). The **if** / **else** block checks whether a **FILENAME** has been set; if it hasn't, then the default of 'SenseLog' is used. The current date and time is also added to the file name.

Finally, the **file_setup** function is called and given the file name that was decided upon in the previous **if** / **else** block.

The last step is to change some of the logic inside the **while True:** loop. You need to make it collect **sense_data**, then use the **log_data** function to convert the **sense_data** into CSV form and add the the current **batch_data**. Once the data is logged, the program checks whether the size of **batch_data** exceeds the **WRITE_**

Fig 4 The code will now output something that is much more readable than the raw data

space-pet.py - /home/pi/space-pet.py (3.4.2)

File Edit Format Run Options Windows Help

```
from sense_hat import SenseHat
import time

sense = SenseHat()

p = (204, 0, 204) # Pink
g = (0, 102, 102) # Gray
w = (200, 200, 200) # White
y = (204, 204, 0) # Yellow
e = (0, 0, 0) # Empty

pet1 = [
    e, e, e, e, e, e, e, e,
    p, e, e, e, e, e, e, e,
    e, p, e, e, p, e, p, e,
    e, p, g, g, p, y, y, e,
    e, g, g, g, y, w, y, g,
    e, g, g, g, g, y, y, e,
    e, g, e, g, e, g, e, e,
    e, e, e, e, e, e, e, e
    ]
```

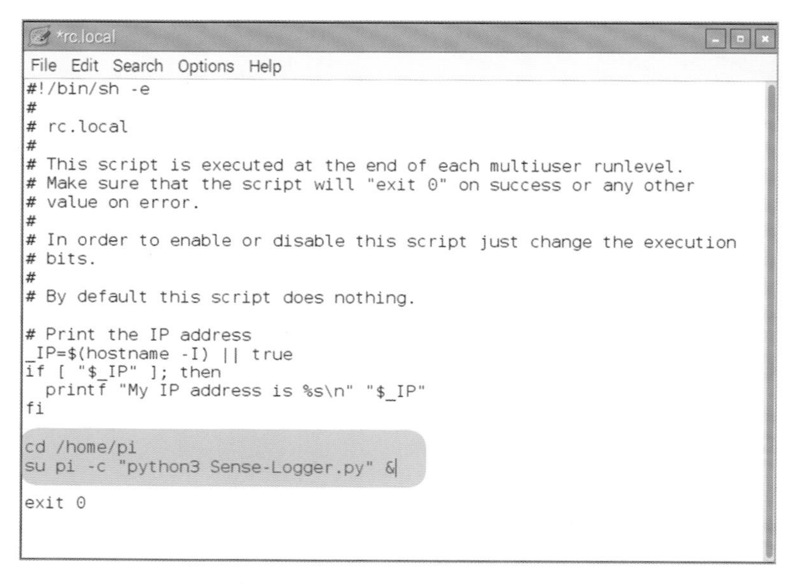

Fig 5 Add lines to rc.local to start the logger upon bootup

FREQUENCY setting; if so, the data is written to a file and **batch_data** is reset.

Your **while True:** loop should be updated to look like this...

```
while True:
  sense_data = get_sense_data()
  log_data()

  if len(batch_data) >= WRITE_FREQUENCY:
      print("Writing to file..")
      with open(filename,"a") as f:
          for line in batch_data:
              f.write(line + "\n")
          batch_data = []
```

The line **print("Writing to file..")** is optional, but it will show whenever data is being written. The line **with open(filename,"a") as f:** opens the file in **append** mode, which adds the data at the end point of the file rather than overwriting. Your code should start looking like **Fig 4**.

When running the program, you should simply see the messages saying 'Writing to file...' every so often. You can stop logging by pressing CTRL+C.

Starting on boot

It's quite likely that you won't want to need to have a screen, keyboard, and mouse handy every time you want to log data. A handy way to avoid this is to have your program run whenever your Raspberry Pi boots up. To do this, you will first need to open a Terminal window and enter the command **`sudo leafpad /etc/rc.local`**. The rc.local script is the last startup script to load as the Raspberry Pi boots. Anything you add to this script will load on boot. Once Leafpad has loaded, you should add two lines like the ones shown in Fig 5.

The first line changes to the directory where your data logger script is stored.

The second line changes to the pi user and runs the command **`python3 Sense-Logger.py`**; the **&** symbol makes this command run as a background task and allows the Raspberry Pi to continue with other tasks.

You'll need to update these lines to reflect the name and location of your program. The next time your Raspberry Pi boots, it should automatically start logging data.

Collect your data

Conduct an experiment involving a change in one condition, in order to measure and collect data. You could:

- Place your Raspberry Pi in the fridge and record the ambient temperature. What happens when you open the door? How quickly does the temperature inside the fridge return to normal?

- Drop your Raspberry Pi from a height and track the changes in orientation and acceleration (ensure you protect your Raspberry Pi carefully before dropping it).

- Send your Raspberry Pi into the atmosphere using a high-altitude balloon and explore the changes in temperature, pressure, and humidity throughout the flight.